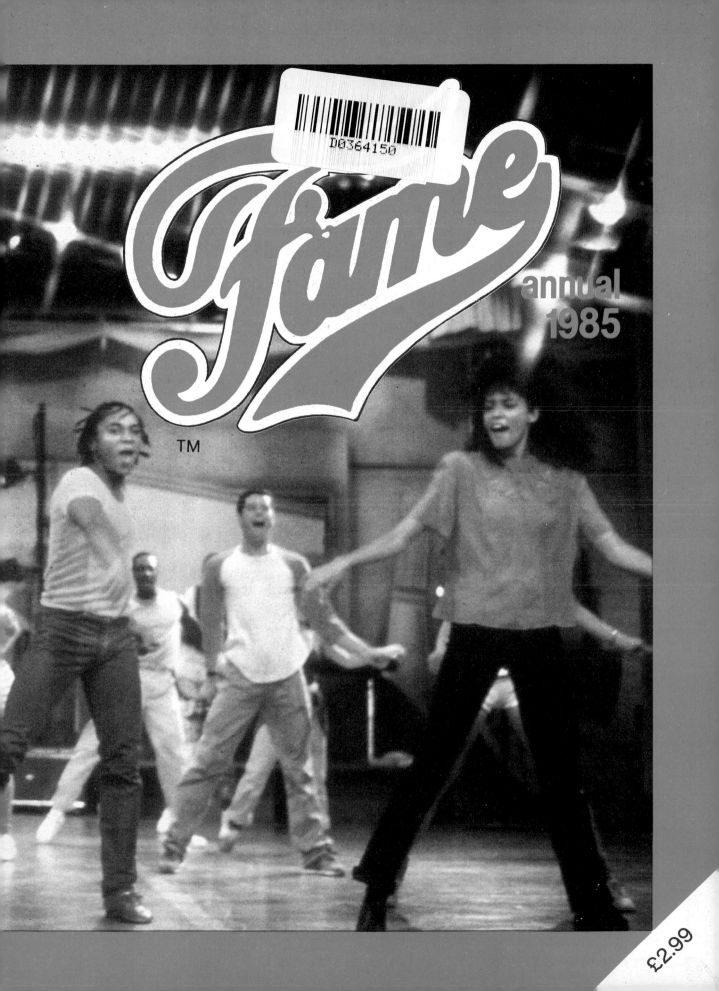

Fame

annual 1985

TM

£2.99

© Transworld Feature Syndicate

Contents

Copyright © MCMLXXXIV by MGM/VA Entertainment Co.
All rights reserved throughout the world.
Published in Great Britain by
World International Publishing Limited,
P.O. Box 111, Great Ducie Street, Manchester M60 3BL.
Printed in Italy.
SBN 7235 6724 7.

MORGAN STEVENS

Morgan Stevens was born and brought up in Knoxville, Tennessee and, though still young, he's had a lot of acting experience.

He has appeared in American imports *Quincy* and *Hellinger's Law,* and has taken a starring role in three tv movies that were inspired by the very popular and long-running series *The Waltons.*

He has appeared on the big cinema screen too, notably in *Haunted Planet* and *Up River.*

Who better then that this experienced young actor to play drama coach David Reardon in *Fame?*

When a word can paint a thousand pictures...

"Leroy Johnson!" Miss Sherwood's voice was loud and angry, and tinged with more than a little exasperation. Leroy pretended not to hear, keeping his head well down and rubbing his forehead with his hands so his eyes were hidden. He had hoped to get through the lesson without Miss Sherwood noticing him. He'd failed by two minutes.

"Leroy," repeated Miss Sherwood. "Have you or have you not brought your paper with you – yes or no?"

Leroy looked around, coughed, scratched his ear, blinked, and finally took his pencil out of his mouth.

"Do you mean yes I have or yes I haven't?" he asked, playing for time. The look on Miss Sherwood's face told him it would be a close-run thing. "Or no, I have, but I left it with my other stuff in the –"

The bell rang and Leroy led the rush for the door.

"Johnson," said Miss Sherwood firmly. "I'd like a word with you."

Leroy stayed behind and, as Miss Sherwood watched him pacing back and forwards, she could almost feel the waves of anger and frustration in him rippling just below the surface. Some of her own anger was replaced by concern.

"Leroy," she said gently, "you know that if you don't put in a paper I can't give you a mark. Your failure here could follow you round for a long time."

"You think I don't know that?"

"If you could just give me something ... anything ... to mark, it would be a step forward. Remember, one good word is worth a hundred bad books. You've got to start somewhere. It doesn't matter what it is. Just write something that shows you know about the power of words."

"They sure got me beat," Leroy admitted. "Sometimes I think it might be better to walk."

"You can't do that, Leroy. Start small. Just give me something, OK?"

Leroy shrugged. "I'll try, Miss Sherwood," he said. "I can't promise I'll succeed, but I promise I'll try."

Miss Sherwood smiled. "You do that," she said. "It would be an awful waste if you had to leave without giving it your best."

When Leroy reached the dance class Lydia Grant was already hard at work, teaching her pupils some new steps.

"Ah, Leroy," she said when Leroy walked in, "I'd like you to demonstrate those steps we were practising yesterday."

Leroy nodded and Lydia switched on the tape. The heavy, resonant base of a ska rhythm filled the room. Leroy stood with his feet slightly apart and his body bent forward, snapping up and down to the rhythm and popping his neck in and out like a turkey. Every third beat he would jerk his body erect and wiggle his shoulders as though he had just stepped into a cold shower. When the tape finished Lydia clapped her hands.

"That's excellent, Leroy," she said. "Perhaps you'd like to explain the steps to the rest of the class?"

"Well," said Leroy, "first of all you've got to imagine you swallowed a giant jumping bean, and that you're itching all over . . ." His voice became faint as he lost himself once again in the magic of dance.

As the others practised the steps, Lydia kept her glittering almond shaped eyes firmly on Leroy. She knew how close he was to being thrown out of the school, and she was deeply worried that his instinctive, inspirational talent would be lost to the world. She could sense the tremendous tension underneath his relaxed, free-flowing dancing. When the lesson ended she took him to one side.

"Is something bothering you, boy?" she asked.

Leroy made as if to leave. "It's lunch time and I've got an important meeting," he said curtly.

"Is it the show?" asked Lydia. Leroy was scheduled to play a large part in the show at the end of the term.

"The show don't bother me at all," said Leroy.

"It should do, honey," said Lydia. Leroy caught the look of genuine worry in her eyes. He rubbed the back of his neck with his hand. Lydia could see something was bothering him.

"Miss Grant . . ." he began haltingly, unsure whether he should go on. Lydia's hand on his forearm told him he should. "Miss Grant," he repeated, "if you had to choose between your career and . . . and somebody else's life . . .?" As his voice haltingly faded away Leroy raised his eyebrows and searched Lydia's face for an answer. Her normal, rock-hard composure seemed to crack a little.

"Things aren't usually that simple, Leroy," she said.

Leroy shrugged her hand off his arm. "I mean, I don't know if I'm going to make it. The chances are a million to one against. Should I hang on to that one chance when I know if I let it go I could save someone's life?"

"You want to tell me about it?" asked Lydia.

Leroy's body slumped and he looked up at the ceiling. Lydia could see tears welling up in his sad, black eyes. For all his street-smart toughness she was reminded that Leroy was still growing up. And then Leroy's jaw set in a firm line, he picked up his jacket, and ran for the door. "Naah – forget it. Like I said," he explained over his shoulder, "I got an appointment."

Leroy sprinted down the corridor, anxious not to be late for his meeting on the school steps. As he ducked round one corner he bumped into the figure of Quentin Morloch, who was hurrying in the opposite direction. The vice principal's papers went flying in the air and he was dumped unceremoniously on to the hard floor. By the time he had struggled to his

feet all he could see of his unwitting assailant was Leroy's back as the young dancer bounded down the stairs. At the school steps Leroy saw a small girl anxiously looking at a Mickey Mouse watch. When she saw Leroy, her face lit up in a bright smile.

"I thought you weren't coming," she said.

Leroy smiled and ruffled her hair as they walked down the street. "Have you ever known me to break a promise?"

When Morloch reached the staff lunch room, his mind was made up. Johnson would have to go. Sure, he was a good dancer, but his behaviour was wrong. So was his attitude. And it wasn't as if he hadn't been given a chance. The kid had had more breaks than Minnesota Fats. Something had to be done before he affected the morale of the whole school. It had been the same with baseball clubs. You can have one guy who's a genius, but if he doesn't pull with the rest of the team he's more trouble than he's worth. These thoughts were at the forefront of his mind when he spoke to Miss Sherwood.

"Are you going to give Johnson a mark?" he asked.

Miss Sherwood looked up from the tomato she was slicing in readiness for her salad. "I don't think I've got a choice," she said sadly. "If he doesn't turn in a paper I'll have to fail him."

"Do you think he's going to turn a paper in?"

Miss Sherwood slowly shook her head. "No," she said simply.

"Then why should we wait until the end of term?" said Morloch. "Johnson is a disruptive influence. I'm afraid he'll have to go."

Shorofsky looked up from the table, where he had been scribbling on a music score. "When do you propose that Mr Johnson leaves?" he asked.

"Now."

Shorofsky placed his pencil on the table and leaned back in his chair. "Is it fair to get rid of him while he still thinks there's time to make good?"

Morloch shrugged as Lydia came in, rubbing her hair with a towel. She stood next to Miss Sherwood, opened a flask and poured herself a mug of thin, clear soup. "I'm worried about Leroy," she said, blowing at the soup. "I think he's in some kind of trouble."

The other teachers exchanged apprehensive glances.

"He's in more trouble than he thinks," said Morloch.

Lydia put her cup down. "What do you mean?" she asked menacingly.

Morloch and Miss Sherwood tried to explain. The three of them were still arguing as they made their way down the corridor for the afternoon's lessons.

And that's where Doris overheard them.

At lunch the following day Danny, Doris, Coco, Holly and Chris were discussing what could be done. Leroy had not turned up for school.

"We could have somebody write a paper for Leroy to hand in," suggested Holly.

Doris shook her head. "It wouldn't work. Leroy wouldn't buy it. He's too proud."

They pondered the problem in silence. Coco was the first to spot the little girl standing in the doorway, looking frightened and confused. She got up and crossed the lunch room. "Hiya, girl," she said with a big, bright smile. "You come to enrol?"

The girl smiled back. "I'm too young," she said.

"Don't you believe it. In this business you can be washed up before your skin clears. What can I do for you?"

"I'm looking for Leroy Johnson."

As Coco led the girl to the table she learned her name was Mimi and that she'd been meeting Leroy every lunchtime that week.

"What for?" asked Danny as the girl settled into a seat. Her face barely peeped over the table.

"He's been helping my brother. They used to be friends . . . before my brother got sick. My brother used to be so active, but now he just lies in bed at home and mopes. It's only when he and Leroy talk about the old times that he gets happy."

"What's your brother's name?" asked Doris.

"Tony," said the little girl. "But people used to know him as Sheppo."

"Sheppo the artist?" asked Danny. At one time Sheppo's multi-coloured action scenes had decorated every spare surface in the South Bronx.

"He was a dancer too," said Coco, "one of the original breakers. Leroy told me that's how he got to know him."

"That's right," agreed the girl. "At one time they were going to form a dancing group. But then Leroy got accepted here and my brother got sick."

"What's wrong with him?"

"His kidneys. He's got no insurance for the treatment. Most of his old friends are too busy getting famous to remember him and Tony's too stubborn to ask for help."

Suddenly Danny got to his feet. "I've got an idea," he said. "I've got a free class first, so cover for me in music if I'm late."

"Hey – where are you going?" asked Doris, but Danny was already half way to the door, and within minutes he was working up his anger as he made his way to Soap's Gallery on King Street. Although he had never met Sheppo, he'd always liked his work. Sheppo had done more than anyone to brighten up the mean streets of his childhood. Sheppo was fearless. He'd go anywhere there was a good surface. His feats of daring were part of local legend. He'd even painted teardrops on the Statue of Liberty. By the time Danny got to the gallery he was in a righteous fervour.

Soap's Gallery had started life as part of a multi-storey car park. It had been in turn a warehouse, a disco and a dancing school. Now it was the baddest art gallery in town, and as Danny climbed the long ramp to the entrance the small groups of mean-looking men, lounging against the walls in the gloom, made him momentarily lose heart. And then he thought of all that Sheppo had tried to do and his courage returned. These guys called themselves revolutionary artists? They claimed they were working for a better world? Danny was going to give them a chance to prove it.

Back at school, Leroy's sudden re-appearance caused an uproar. He refused to say where he had been and Morloch had ordered him from the premises. Doris had persuaded him to stay and was now leading a delegation of students to Morloch's office. When he let them in, the look on his face let them know he was in no mood to be trifled with.

"What's that child doing in here?" he asked testily, nodding towards Mimi.

"She's part of the reason you can't let Leroy go," said Doris.

"Can't?" asked Morloch.

"Mimi — you tell him," said Holly.

Mimi stepped forward.

"Hold it," Leroy butted in.

"You don't have to say nothing, Mimi. I'm out of the school and that's that. I'll be out anyway if I don't turn in a paper. There's no point dragging this thing out. These are the breaks."

Morloch studied Leroy's face. It seemed Leroy really was ready to go.

"Wait a minute, Johnson," he said. "I'd be obliged if you'd wait around until I've heard what this girl has to say."

"No!" said Leroy firmly. He knelt down and took Mimi's hands in his own. His voice was soft and tender, and close to cracking. "I'm sorry, Mimi — I was down at the hospital today. They said they couldn't take my kidney. It wasn't the right match for Sheppo."

"Then . . . then . . ." Mimi looked heartbroken. Morloch coughed nervously and Doris and Bruno shuffled their feet until a

commotion in the doorway made them look up.

In the doorway stood Danny with Joe "Soap" Mancuso, owner of Soap's Gallery.

"Then nothing!" said Danny cheerfully. "Joe's got something to tell you."

They all looked at Joe, who smiled sheepishly. "Well," he began, "there's a whole bunch of nonsense talked about art, and we at Soap's Gallery are trying to get away from all that. We don't like critics. You either do it or you don't. If you kicked the nonsense out of your average critic you could bury him in a matchbox."

"Joe," interrupted Danny, rolling his eyes. "Why don't you get to the point?"

"All right. When Danny came and told me about Sheppo, I rang around the artists who exhibit with me. Each one of them offered to

donate at least one picture for me to auction. The proceeds will go towards Sheppo's treatment, and if everything goes right we might be able to get enough for a down payment on a dialysis machine for the neighbourhood."

The whole room burst out in a wave of spontaneous cheering. Danny waved his hands in the air. "That's not all," he said. "There were some of Sheppo's old break-dancing friends down there. They didn't know that Sheppo had been ill. They promised to put on a free show for Sheppo's benefit. And get this – they want me to MC and you guys to do the closing number."

"Us?" gasped Doris in mock horror. "Headlining over some of the country's hottest chart acts? Pinch me, someone, I've got to be dreaming!"

"Did you say pinch or punch?"

asked Danny. Coco picked Mimi up and held her in her arms as Miss Sherwood entered with some papers.

"Well," said Coco, "it looks like everything turned out right in the end."

"Not everything," said Morloch. "There's still the matter of Leroy's English paper. Is that right, Miss Sherwood?"

Miss Sherwood nodded. "Well, Leroy?" she asked.

Leroy leaned his head to one side. "You said that it's not the quantity of words that matter, but the quality, right?"

"Right."

"Well, I was telling Sheppo about everything you said, how everything you write has got to be to the point, how the least number of words often catches the meaning better than some long-winded description, how one well-chosen word can be worth more than a book full of bad ones. I was talking to Sheppo about how important it was for me to make a start, and he said –"

"Leroy – is this another of your excuses?"

"No, ma'am, I said I'd try, and I have."

"I hope so, Leroy, because if you haven't done a paper that shows that at least you've been thinking about this problem; if you haven't even tried to figure out a way to get started on your project; if you've flunked out again, then I'm sorry, but this will be your last day in this school."

Leroy fished a sheet of paper from his pocket and handed it to Miss Sherwood. Scrawled in the middle was the solitary word, "IF".

Miss Sherwood stared at it for a few seconds and then smiled resignedly.

"What do you say, Miss Sherwood?" asked Leroy. "Will it do?"

Miss Sherwood smiled broadly, and shook her head. "It won't do, Leroy. It's not enough for a pass."

"But it's a start, right?"

"It's a start, Leroy," she said grudgingly. "It's a start."

Valerie Landsburg was brought up in California in a showbusiness environment, for her father is successful producer Alan Landsburg, and right from the start the school subject that interested her most was drama.

While she was at college studying psychology she worked part-time for him as a production assistant, so the world of film is a very familiar one for her. Valerie abandoned her college studies when she landed her first part in the disco film *Thank God It's Friday* — and she hasn't looked back since, acting in theatre, film, and now *Fame*.

But she insists that her father has no unfair influence on her career; his name hasn't got her parts. "I read and test for parts just like everybody else," she says.

In fact Valerie tested for the part of Doris Schwartz in the original film of Fame, and was rejected, even though she knew she was right for the part. Then, three years on, Valerie tested for the TV show. "I thought, if they don't cast me, I get out of the business," she remembers. "They can't possibly find anybody who can do this any better than I can."

The producers agreed, and Valerie has gone on to create a very strong and sympathetic character in fast-talking, heart-of-gold Doris. She loves the show, and loves acting. "I'm lucky to be paid for doing something that I would do for free. I'm in the only profession (apart from pro sports) where adults get paid for doing what children do for free."

The Stars of Fame:
CARLO IMPERATO

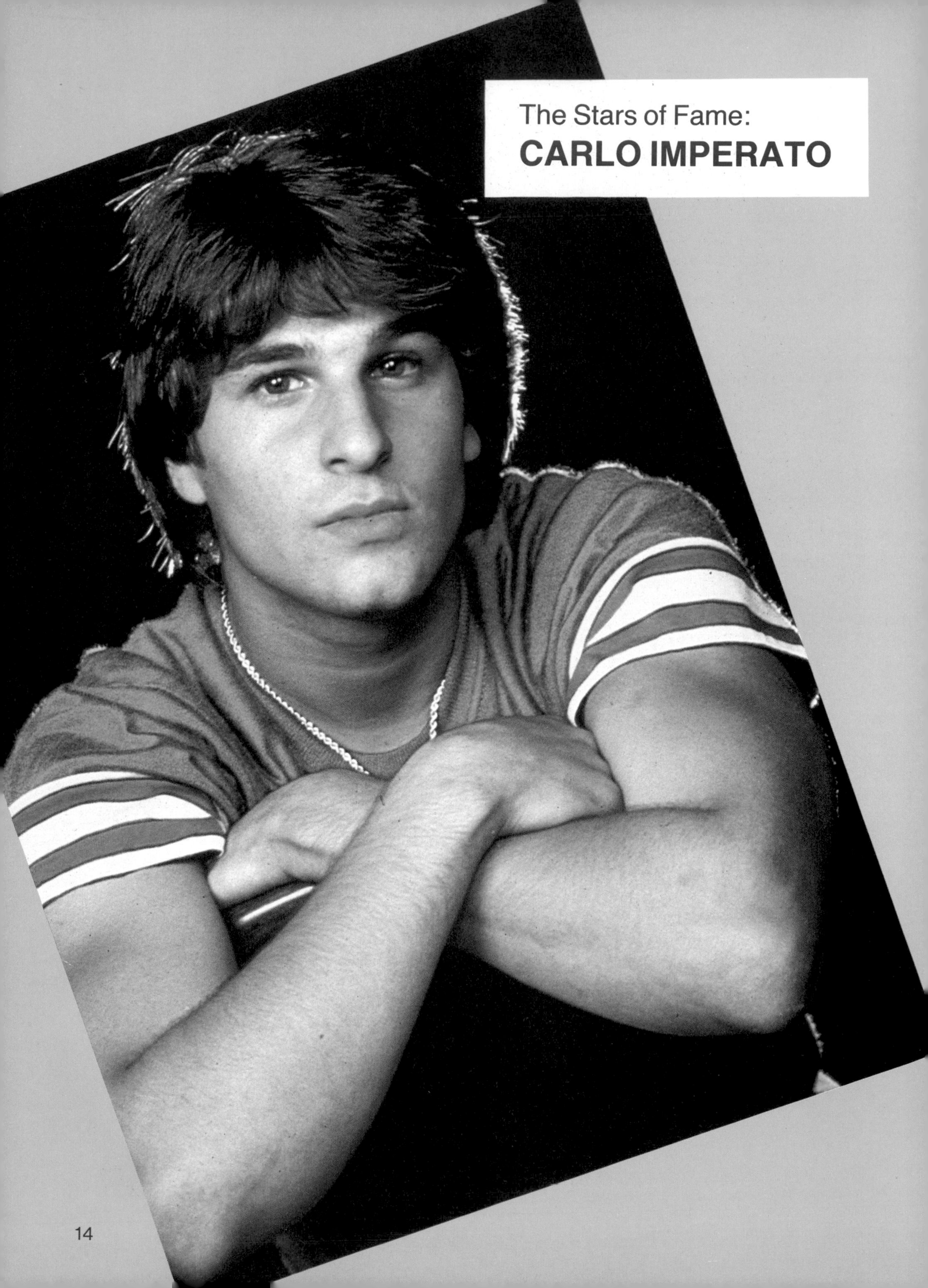

Carlo Imperato was born and brought up in the Bronx, an area of New York, and attended Columbus High School. While a student there he heard that auditions were being held for an off-Broadway show called *The Runaways*. Though he had had no previous acting experience Carlo won a part in the show, and stayed with it for its one-year run.

The acting bug had now bitten, and Carlo decided to continue his education at a special theatre school, the Professional Children's School.

He made his television debut in a movie for NBC, *The Hayburners*, and acted in the feature films *Enormous Changes at the Last Minute*, and *The Man in the Santa Suit*, but it is *Fame* which has really brought fame for Carlo, his portrayal of wise-cracking Danny Amatullo making him one of the most popular members of the cast.

Carlo loves acting above anything else, and enjoyed touring the world with the Fame stage show, but when he has a little spare time he enjoys playing soccer, basketball and American football.

Good Timing

"It's really very simple," explained Danny, lobbing the remains of his cheeseburger breakfast into a nearby garbage can as he and Doris stepped onto the street, heading for the school. "Take eggs, for example. Have you any idea why so many people eat hens' eggs?"

"Because they're too small to be used as footballs?" asked Doris, flicking through a well-worn copy of *Othello* to find a relevant speech. Across the road, the students of the School of the Arts were milling round its grey stone steps, waiting to go in. Leroy and Coco were leaping round a ghetto-blaster that sent Lionel Richie's distinctive phrasing ringing through the crisp morning air, two first-year students were working on a mime, another was practising her body-popping and Chris was strutting back and forth to some hidden rhythm on a Walkman. Danny was beginning to move to the beat when the loud blaring sound of a car horn shattered the chaotic harmony of the

scene and he and Doris were forced into an undignified scramble to avoid a light blue sedan, racing to beat the lights at the next intersection.

"Women drivers!" shouted Danny from the safety of the kerb.

"It was a man, you chauvinist piglet," Doris pointed out. "I saw him quite clearly."

"Yeah? Well, I bet his mother taught him how to drive," said Danny, before returning to his discourse on hens' eggs, and why people eat them. "You see, the reason that people eat so many hens' eggs is that —"

"Cockerels don't lay them?" Doris suggested pointedly.

Danny held out his hands in a plea for patience. "When a hen lays an egg, it squawks," he explained. "That makes the egg easy to find. When a goose lays an egg it doesn't say anything at all."

"Perhaps geese don't share your inimitable grasp of the English language."

"I mean that if you wanna sell eggs, you've got to advertise. It's no good hiding your light in the bush. A bird in the hand and all that. You've got to promote yourself in this business."

"So?"

Danny fielded a basketball that had strayed from a street-corner game and dribbled twice round Doris.

"Promotion is the key to success, Doris," he continued, bouncing the ball from hand to hand. "If you don't make a noise nobody's going to listen. And then you end up like all the other turkeys."

"So much for woodcraft," said Doris, breaking off and walking over to Holly, who sat hunched over a book in the cold morning sun, muttering over Hamlet's soliloquy in preparation for her English project. Danny dribbled the basketball up the street and took a shot at the rusty basket attached to the wall. The ball bounced against the brickwork, rolled round the rim, and flopped out.

"You always that bad?" asked a young Spanish boy with a beret pulled down over the side of his face. "Or have you been taking lessons?"

"One to one – the first to three?" queried Danny, by way of a challenge. The boy — Pete — grinned his acceptance, flipped the ball through his legs, dummied Danny, cut inside – and scored.

Pete scored the second as well, but with dogged determination and a little bit of luck Danny pulled back all-square. When a long-shot from Pete bobbled clear, Danny sprang upward to try and flip the rebound in, but Pete's skinny fingers beat him to it and he fell clumsily to the ground, badly grazing the knuckles of his hand.

"That was a foul!" complained Danny in time-honoured tradition.

Pete shook his head. "That was no foul. You timed your jump all wrong."

"My timing's perfect," Danny protested.

"Oh yeah?" Pete nodded towards the school and Danny turned. The steps were empty. He'd been so busy he hadn't heard the bell. As he ran towards school the derisive laughter of the young basketball players followed him down the street.

When Danny arrived in the music class, ten minutes late, Professor Shorofsky glanced pointedly at his watch without breaking the impressive flow of his words. Danny meekly made his way to his seat.

"The ear is an extremely delicate and complicated instrument. After the pinna collects the sound waves, the tympanum – with the help of the ear ossicles – transmits the vibrations to the base of the cochlea, which, in turn, converts them into nervous impulses that are passed along the auditory nerve to the brain. Can you understand what I'm saying, Amatullo?"

"I can hear it, but I can't understand it."

"I'm talking about the human ear."

"I've got acute hearing."

"You're not wearing an earring," whispered Doris.

Danny abandoned his attempt at a low profile.

17

open up hitherto unknown depths in music for the listener."

"But surely it's just a series of notes?"

Shorofsky sighed and walked over to the piano. He played several notes at irregular intervals.

"What was I playing?" he asked. The class remained silent. Shorofsky then picked up a ruler and rapped out a rhythm on the top of a desk. It was immediately recognisable as *Oh, Susannah.*

"You see," he said. "The notes were right but the timing was wrong. The spaces between the sounds are almost as important as the sounds themselves. Unless you can appreciate nuance and subtlety the quality of your whole life will suffer."

"What's nuance?" asked Danny.

Shorofsky smiled. "It's something that doesn't slap you in the face like a wet kipper. It leans towards delicacy rather than overkill."

"You mean that a song that's got, say, a lot of violins in, that's got a lot of nuance?" asked Danny, trying to show willing.

Shorofsky shook his head. "No. The presence of violins means nothing in itself. It is the way instruments are deployed that is important, not how many instruments are used. More, in musical terms, is not necessarily better. Often it is quite the reverse. The style of much modern music — constructing tunes in the way a greedy child

"Peculiar ears run in our family," he said, mock-serious. "And you've got to admit, ears that run are peculiar. My grandmother had extemely unusual ears. She was so late paying the rent that the landlord said she'd got 200 dollars in arrears."

Professor Shorofsky's sorely tried patience finally snapped. "Amatullo!" he said sternly. "Having chosen to ignore the blatant rudeness of your late arrival, I had hoped you might reciprocate the gesture by paying attention."

"I'm sorry, sir. It's the comedian in me."

"In music, Amatullo, as in comedy, timing is all important. Understanding the sophisticated machinery of the human ear helps concocts a milk shake, piling one glop of sickly rubbish on top of another – indicates a poverty of imagination rather than a creative surplus. If, Amatullo, you approach your comedy in the same way, it would go a long way to explaining why so many of us fear for your future."

Lost for a suitably witty reply, Danny buttoned his lip. As Shorofsky explained how the different horizontal and vertical hearing planes placed paramount importance on the position of instruments on stage, he tried to figure out what someone like W C Fields would make of the professor's view on comedy. After ten minutes he gave it up, gripped with a growing feeling of inadequacy. After all, Fields was a genius, and he was just a kid in school.

But, on the way to the drama class, Danny's spirits were unexpectedly lifted and he began to appreciate some of the benefits of school life when Darlene Rogers stopped him in the corridor. Darlene was the daughter of a well-known L.A. magician and she had promised to lend Danny one of her father's books to help him with a routine he was working on. She also had the brightest blue eyes in the whole school.

"I'm sure I put it in here," she said, rummaging through her bag. "Unless . . . yep . . . typical. I left it in my locker."

They chatted noisily as they walked to the downstairs hallway. There was something about her eyes that put Danny at his ease. When she finally found the book she gave it to him with a smile like sparkling wine.

"There's a Jerry Lewis retrospective at the Film Forum tonight. You wanna come?" The words were out before Danny had even thought of them.

Darlene's smile faded from her mouth, but her eyes still shone.

"I'm sorry, Danny," she said. "Any other time I'd love to. But my dad's flying in tonight. He and Mom are thinking of getting back together again."

"Bad timing, huh?" smiled Danny ruefully. "Some other time, maybe?"

"Sure."

By the time Danny reached the drama class it was well under way.

"You're late," said Reardon.

"Sorry," said Danny, putting the magic book down on his desk.

"Perhaps you'd like to give us the benefit of your ideas?"

Danny opened his exercise book. "The school's going broke, OK?" he began. Reardon nodded. "And they have to merge with another school to save money. But this other school is for delinquents. They have these great big guys in gangs who terrorise everybody in the school. The teachers have to be armed. Guards with sub-machine guns stand by the desks. Only one guy

– a comedian – keeps the gangs from taking over, and he's in love with the gang-boss's girl-friend . . ." Danny's voice trailed off as Reardon held up his hand.

"West Side Story, it ain't," said Doris.

"But it could work!" Danny protested. "I've thought it out. Most of the action could take place in one classroom, and the storyline could carry plenty of songs and even a comedy slot. And at least it's modern."

"So is cream cheese in aerosol spray cans," said Reardon. "I accept that you've worked hard on this, and apparently you've re-searched it quite well, but as an idea for an end-of-term project it's a little bit . . ."

"Like a milk-shake?" offered Doris gleefully. "With lurid ideas heaped on top of each other like so many scoops of goo?"

"It's a curious analogy, Doris," Reardon remarked. "But not far from the truth. A good idea can lose its impact if it is lost in a tor-rent of other, less good ideas. Good drama relies a lot on –"

"Let me guess," Danny inter-rupted. "Timing?"

"Exactly."

That lunch time, while Coco, Leroy and Chris rehearsed an acrobatic dance number and Doris and Holly swapped wafer-thin sandwiches along with the latest Hollywood gossip, Danny took himself off for a walk. He wanted to get away from the school for a while, to clear his mind of the seemingly endless technicalities that went hand in hand with becoming a successful performing artist.

Danny padded alongside the cratered city roads, trying to re-build his confidence. He had started the day in such a carefree style. He'd worked hard at his projects, he'd thought up a couple of neat one-liners, and he fully ex-pected it to be one of those days when everyone recognised the fact that not only was he a natural comic talent, but also an extreme-ly hard worker and an all-round good guy to boot. He smiled. Hu-man beings are the only animals with the ability to laugh – and the only animals with pretensions worth laughing at.

Danny suddenly realised he was hungry. Less than ten yards ahead, a man in a black bobble hat stood studying the outside menu at a burger bar. Danny hur-ried in and ordered a coke and a hot dog with all the trimmings. He was dipping into his wallet to pay when there was a sudden shout, and in the mirror behind the coun-ter he saw the man from outside, with his woollen hat pulled down over his face, waving a large pistol in the air. A sudden eerie silence descended on the scene.

"This is a stick-up!" yelled the gunman. The man behind the counter emptied the till with shak-ing hands and Danny tried to slip his wallet back in his pocket. He wasn't quick enough. The man rapped his shoulder with the butt of his gun and grabbed Danny's

wallet as it fell on the counter.

"Hey! That's mine!" Danny complained.

"Tough break, sap," said the gunman, seizing the rest of the money and backing off towards the door. "It was your bad luck to be in the wrong place —"

"Yeah, I know," Danny finished for him. "At the wrong time."

By the time Danny had given the police a description of the man, he was late yet again. As he hurried back to the school he was seething. He had particularly wanted to be present for the English class because he had worked so hard on his project. It was the one way he could salvage a disastrous day. The subject had been 'Shakespeare in modern America', and although he didn't know a lot about Shakespeare, he figured he'd got modern America pretty well covered. The way he saw it, if Bill was alive today, he'd be working in Hollywood. And if *Macbeth* had been a hit, there would have to be a *Macbeth II*. It was with this in mind that he'd written a voice-over for a trailer for *Macbeth II*. He ran it over in his mind as he rushed through the city streets.

"You laughed at *A Midsummer Night's Dream* . . . you cried at *Hamlet*. Now, you can chill once again to the knife-wielding Monarch of Murder — *Macbeth!* In dank Glamis Castle a warrior king and his voluptuous wife unleash a blood-drenched orgy of supernatural terror when they fight once again to cheat the curse of the witches. Death stalks the bat-

tlements, ghosts prowl the eerie passageways, evil and intrigue lurk in the flickering shadows as, outside, the creeping terror of a living forest turns paradise into a garden of evil! This unrelenting saga of vengeance and disaster sends the scare-o-meter past overload into the forbidden zone. If *Macbeth* scared you — *Macbeth II* will have you climbing the walls. The king is back!"

He liked it. He'd put a lot of work into it and he reckoned it was relevant and pretty funny. And there was nothing in it about timing. He looked at his watch as he neared the school. Fifteen minutes left. There was still time! Even Miss Sherwood would have to give him credit. It would knock her socks off!

Danny burst into the classroom, gabbling his excuse.

Miss Sherwood told him to sit down.

"I want to read my project," he said.

"Very commendable, Danny," said Miss Sherwood, "but you'll have to wait your turn. We're listening to what Doris has to say."

And Doris had plenty to say. She went on and on about the relevance of Shakespeare to today's world, how the bard had laid bare the human condition five hundred years ago and still people ignored his message, indulging the evil in them until the human race found itself on a fast train to oblivion.

After a particularly virulent attack on the existence of the diet industry when half the world was undernourished, Doris finally sat down.

Danny was first to his feet.

Miss Sherwood folded. "All right, Amatullo — the floor's yours."

Danny beamed. At last. He

cleared his throat. "It seems to me, that if someone of Shakespeare's talent was alive today," he began, "that the one place he could exploit his talent to the full would be . . ." He paused to give his words maximum effect, and the bell rang. "Hollywood!" he shouted. "Listen up, you guys, this is good!"

But his words were lost in the hubbub of a class set free.

The next day Danny got up early. He was feeling confident, victorious even. During the night he had dug up some quote from Cobbett about the uselessness of music. He'd also got a list of the biggest grossing movies of all time that shot Reardon's timing rap right out of the water. He'd done

some work on the history of the catch-phrase that he felt sure he could draw Miss Sherwood on to once he'd softened her up with his Macbeth stuff. As he set off in plenty of time for the first lesson he felt better armed than an octopus.

So the others thought he was a clown. That was his ambition, wasn't it? His target was Vegas, the top, and the stuff he gave them was just a spin-off, the mechanics that every pro has in his armoury, one liners and asides he'd learned on the way, the kind of stuff Pavlov gave his dog. The real work needed a more sophisticated audience, people who would go with the flow, with no mention of petty rules like timing.

When Danny reached the school he was surprised to see that the only people in the street were Pete and his pals playing basketball. Surely he wasn't that early? He checked his watch. Dead on time. He shook his wrist and put his watch to his ear. It was working perfectly. He peered into the school hall. It was empty. . . .

And then it hit him. Saturday. Perfect timing, wrong day. The school was shut. He sat down on the steps with his head in his hands, laughing fit to bust. If he needed proof that he could raise a laugh, this was it. He was still laughing when he felt a gentle touch on his shoulder.

"Darlene!" He laughed, looking once again into those bright blue eyes, like teaspoons filled with the Caribbean. "What are you doing here?"

"Just walking," she said with a smile. "I've not met you at an awkward time, have I?"

Danny got up and linked her arm as they walked past the basketball game. "Not at all," he said, still laughing, "I'd say the time is pretty near perfect!"

The Stars of Fame:
KEN SWOFFORD

The not-so-popular vice principal of the School of the Arts is played by versatile actor Ken Swofford, a performer with a long list of film and tv credits to his name.

His film appearances include *Annie, S.O.B., Bless the Beasts and Children, The Andromeda Strain* and *The Domino Principal*, and he has had parts in tv films including *I Want to Live* and *Young Joe Kennedy.*

He has starred in as a regular or had recurring roles in many tv series, too, including *Ellery Queen, Petrocelli, The Rookies* and *Rich Man, Poor Man II* – and now, of course, *Fame.*

The Stars of Fame:
CAROL MAYO JENKINS

Carol Mayo Jenkins is an actress through and through, and will act, in her own words: "Anywhere someone will put up a stage." She is a truly successful actress, and has tackled roles in the classics to contemporary drama, seldom finding herself out of work.

She loves working in front of a live audience. "There's nothing like actually feeling audience reactions," she says. "Nothing like taking a bow to the sound of applause."

She became bored when she played a long-running role in a daytime TV drama series, but hasn't been bored in *Fame*, which she feels comes closest to live theatre.

"There's so much energy and excitement during the production, every day on the set is like opening night. That feeling is like food and drink to any actor."

"No speak the English, eh?" puffed Adrian.

Doris responded with a smile of blank incomprehension.

They plodded onwards together.

"I suppose you could consider yourself lucky," Adrian went on. "Not being able to understand me, that is. I'm not very good company these days. Haven't been the same since my wife left me. That's why I'm trying to get back into shape, trying to put some zing back in my life. Where did you say you were from?"

Once again Doris smiled her idiot smile.

"Sorry, I forgot," gasped Adrian. "I guess I'm losing my grip. Things seem to be travelling too fast for me to get a handle on them. Even my work's slipping. I used to be the best in the business. Now I'm down to producing adverts. Using Verdi to sell chocolate bars. You don't happen to know where I could find two cute teeny-bopping dance-trained space cadets by tomorrow lunchtime, do you?"

Doris pulled up, a greedy smile on her lips and a look of surprised joy in her eyes.

Adrian apologised once again. "I'm sorry. I forgot. I didn't mean to carry on this way. I thought it would help to speak to someone, even someone who doesn't understand what I'm saying."

"Are you a producer?" asked Doris. "Really, truly, a producer?"

"Sure. I used to be pretty big cheese around here. Now people think I'm jinxed."

"And you want two people to act as spacemen in an advertisement?"

"Sure. But – I thought you couldn't speak English?"

"Never mind what you thought, Mr Spinks," said Doris, ushering the exhausted man towards a nearby bench. "You and I are going to talk business."

Back in school, Leroy and Dwight were talking business of a different kind. "You can do it, man – I know you can," said Leroy encouragingly.

Dwight seemed unsure. "It's not as easy as you think," he said. "I can programme the computer to do it for you, but there's an operator coming to look at it this afternoon, and anyway I've got to feed in the right words first."

"I got the words," said Leroy. "Cool . . . loose . . . boogaloo . . ."

Dwight finally relented. "OK, Leroy, I'll do what I can."

When Doris returned in time for lessons she was carrying a bag full of space gear and wearing a smile as wide as a bus.

Danny caught up with her in the downstairs hallway. "What you got there?" he asked, nodding at the bag.

"Some spacesuits – Danny, I've cracked it!"

"What do you mean?"

"I've got us both up for rehearsal tomorrow. For an advert. Chokk-E-Wokks!"

"You don't mean you're going to abandon your hard-earned integrity by trivialising your monumental talents to sell chocolates?"

"You bet I am. Are you in?"

"You bet. Let's try the suits on."

"Not yet. They've got chocolate all over them. I'm going to take them down to the laundry after school."

As Doris walked off to the music class, the narrow trail to stardom opening up into a six-lane highway in her mind, Danny took the opportunity of slipping Chris's dirty jacket in with the spacesuits. No point in wasting good washing time. There'd be plenty of time for extravagance when he was a star.

After school, when Danny and

Doris rushed off to the laundry, Miss Sherwood, Professor Shorofsky and Quentin Morloch enjoyed a cup of coffee in the staff room before going home.

"I think the modern world's passing me by," said Miss Sherwood, puzzling over a sheet of paper. "By the way, how did you get on with the computer? I saw you talking to the operator."

"I played chess with it," said Shorofsky with a sigh.

"And?"

"And when I took its pawn, it moved the king to third base."

"That's nothing," said Morloch. "I asked it the velocity needed for a home run in the Yankee Stadium, and it told me how to do the Funky Chicken!"

A smile spread slowly across Miss Sherwood's face as she read the paper again. "Of course!" she laughed. "That explains it!"

"Explains what?"

"Leroy's paper. He must have got someone to use the computer for him. Listen to this." Miss Sherwood coughed, and began reading in a gravely serious voice. "Mr Bojangles was probably the finest dancer the world has ever seen. He could do the shuggy boogaloo and often moved the king at 152.35 mph to avoid check-mate. His cool diamond knight takes bishop was the most hard hitting example of size of bat used . . ."

She couldn't go on. Tears of laughter were rolling down her cheeks. Shorofsky leant back in his chair, his body shaking, and Morloch pounded the table and roared. It was a good moment to be alive.

In the café across the street from the laundry Danny was thinking much the same thing as he and Bruno discussed whether dollar-sign swimming pools were brash, or just honest.

"I think I'll have mine moon-shaped," said Bruno. "Are you sure they don't want three spacemen?"

"Sorry, Bruno — the concept wouldn't allow it. The script is as finely tuned as a Swiss watch. And they've only got two suits."

"Correction, Amatullo!"

Danny looked up. Doris had returned from the laundry and was standing in the doorway of the café, holding Chris's now mud-coloured jacket in one hand, and in the other, what had once been two bright silver spacesuits. They were now a bedraggled mess, a mottled mixture of drab greens and brown.

"Lost a bit of their sheen, haven't they?" said Danny.

Doris made a peculiar growling sound at the back of her throat. "You loused it up, Amatullo," she said, as if amazed at herself for ever allowing Danny within one hundred miles of her. "I trusted you, and you loused it up!"

"Well . . er . . . yes, Doris — I guess I did."

"What have you got to say about it?"

"Er . . . I . . . er . . ." Danny stood up and looked round him. Bruno was smiling. Doris was advancing. "Er . . . just one thing —" He backed off towards the kitchens. "Is there any way out of here?"

The Stars of Fame:
CINDY GIBB

Cynthia (Cindy) Gibb was born and raised in Connecticut, and started out on her showbusiness career at the age of fourteen as a model. A month after she left high school graduation she exchanged modelling for acting, and joined the cast of the New York-based soap opera *Search for Tomorrow*.

"Being a part of that show was a wonderful learning experience," says Cindy, referring to the two years she spent with the show, but when she heard that there was an opening on *Fame* she decided to try out for it.

"I wanted it bad," said Cindy, "because what I really want to do is sing and dance. I did a screen test in New York and I loved my character, drama student Holly Laird. I was then asked to fly to Los Angeles and test for the role. After that I was asked to test for my singing and dancing abilities, which I did. When I heard that I had the role . . . well, I think it was one of the few times I was speechless!

"I'm so excited about being part of the cast of *Fame* I still can't believe it," says Cindy. I keep thinking I'll wake up and it will all turn out to be a dream! I loved the *Fame* movie and I love the series. I want to sing and dance on *Fame* until I'm too old for the role!"

32

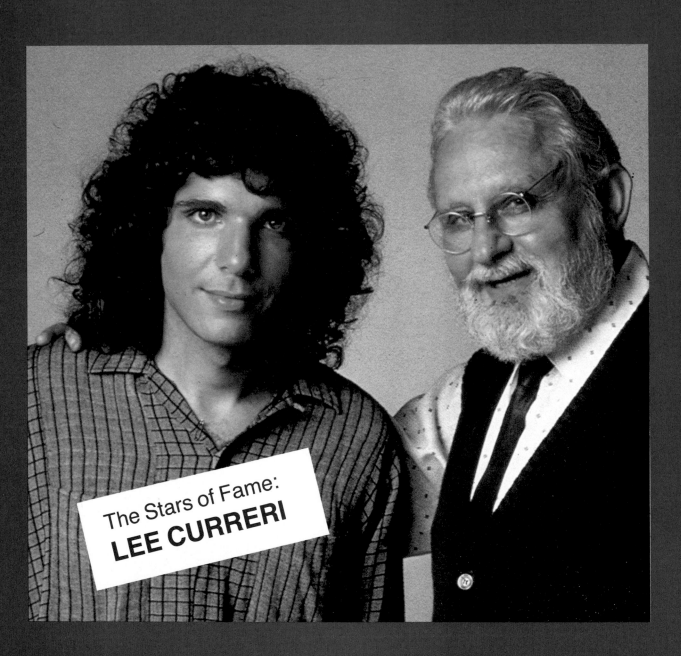

The Stars of Fame:
LEE CURRERI

Music is Lee Curreri's life. When Lee was six a neighbour gave the Curreri family an old piano, and that started his interest in music. While still at school he attended music and acting classes, and this led to Lee's appearance in the *Fame* feature film. His performance in the film was highly rated by the critics, so when NBC came to cast for the Fame series there was really only one person suitable for the part of Bruno Martelli — and that person was Lee.

From the start he made a great impact on the series, not only acting and singing but also writing many original songs.

Unlike Bruno, Lee's interest in music is wide ranging, and he composes in a classical as well as a modern vein. He composed the incidental music for the film version of Chekhov's *The Seagull*, and also wrote the score for the TV film *Bill On His Own* starring Mickey Rooney. "Scoring the music and doing the orchestration was exciting,"

said Lee, "but conducting the 25-piece orchestra was frightening!" He also found time to write, arrange and record a solo album.

"I love acting," says Lee, " and I love being part of *Fame*. But I'm really happiest when I'm thinking and creating, which is what *Fame* has allowed me to do. It's given me the financial status and the time to work on my music. That's why, as far as I'm concerned, the series *can* live forever!"

The Stars of Fame:
ERICA GIMPEL

Erica Gimpel was born and brought up in Manhattan, and attended the School of Performing Arts, the actual school that *Fame* is based on. She did a lot of acting there, but started to major on dancing when she got the part of Coco Hernandez in the show.

She acted as a child, touring in *Porgy and Bess* with her mother (a singer), a period that took her to Portugal and Australia as well as America.

Then it was back to school in New York — at least until the auditions for the *Fame* tv series began, and Erica landed the role that Irene Cara had played in the film.

But even after the great success of *Fame* Erica was keen to continue her education, and between seasons of the series she went back to the School of Performing Arts.

So what of the future? Erica would like to play in a movie or on stage in a role that would show a different side of her range — the classics, maybe. Or, in her own words: "I want to play every character, every type of woman."

come, he realised, for plain speaking. "Mrs Holmes, don't you understand yet? Your nephew Bobby doesn't want to be an entertainer, it's YOU that wants him to be. That's why he hasn't come home. Now, if you promise me you'll let this idea of putting him through the school drop, I'll make you a promise. I'll have him back at your house tomorrow for you. There's just one condition. That whatever he wants to be, whether it's farmer, footballer, or circus acrobat – you let him be it. There

are good people who will take care of him in whatever walk of life he chooses. But if he's not doing what he wants then the game isn't worth playing. I remember our coach saying . . ."

"Now look what you've gone and done, you big lump," said Lydia angrily. "You've made her cry again!"

"Miss Grant," said Quentin stiffly, "if you could explain the duties that our new dance teacher is going to perform during your absence then perhaps you'll let me

get on with my job. Which – in case any of you have forgotten – is trying to make sure this school stays running."

"Mister Morloch," a voice called after him as he left, and he turned to see Mrs Holmes sitting on a metal chair with Lydia's hands on her shoulders. He watched her smile and dab a handkerchief she took from her bag against her eyes. "After my dear Henry, Mister Morloch, I think you're the sweetest man I've ever met."

Her remark had Morloch scowling, then blushing, then laughing, then scowling all the way over to Bruno Martelli's house.

Bruno explained in more detail about Bobby. "He told me right off about how he wanted to be a farmer," he said. "Who'd ever have figured it? I was worried about taking him in at first, I didn't want anyone to get hurt. Now I'm just glad that things have worked out so well. You know that guy Bobby? He's fitted cupboards all along one wall of my bedroom. It takes all kinds. Bobby was so good I got him a job helping fit a refrigeration plant at the local supermarket. The kid's just got an aptitude."

As Bruno spoke, a plan was forming in Quentin Morloch's mind. Bruno was right, he thought, you had to have an aptitude for your job. If you didn't then things were a struggle.

Morloch's chain of thought was interrupted by the front door of the apartment being opened. A thin, straw-haired young man with the same high cheekbones as his aunt came in and then, when he looked at Quentin, his jaw fell open in surprise. "Say, Bruno," he said excitedly, "I didn't know you knew anyone famous. This is Quentin Morloch. You know in his rookie season he came in as relief pitcher and pitched seven straight shutouts? You know I used to have your photograph on the inside of my suitcase lid, Mister Morloch? My dad was a piano player, see, and we used to travel a lot. Mom was a dancer. I used to study the averages when they were working, and then we'd bet nickles and on the day games. I always cleaned up."

Quentin smiled and asked him how he'd like to meet Billy Berg. Bobby asked him if he meant the same Billy Berg who'd played catcher for Morloch in the play-offs.

"None other," said Quentin with a smile. "He's got a farm up in Connecticut. Not an hour's drive from here. I'll take you up there – on one condition."

Bobby asked him what that was.

"Bruno tells me you've got an aptitude for building. I want you to help me build a new music studio at that school you don't want to go to."

Leroy was undisputed dance king at the School of the Arts — until a new dance major came along in the form of Christopher Donlan, rough round the edges from growing up on the streets, and bursting with potential. He's out to snatch Leroy's crown . . .

The actor who portrays Christopher Donlan, Billy Hufsey, is also bursting with talent. Billy is an actor-dancer with wide experience in the business, having appeared in movies like *Off the Wall*, *Graduation Day* and *Clarence and the Ottaway*. He has also appeared in episodes of TV series *Rocco's Star*, *The Righteous Apples* and *General Hospital*.

But his talents don't stop at acting, for Billy was one of the famous Jeff Kutash Dancers, and performed coast to coast across America. And he's an athlete of no mean ability, too: 1971 Ohio State Invitation Bowling Champion, 1978 Ohio Golden Gloves finalist and 1979 US Singles Disco Champion.

Fame is the perfect show for the many and varied talents of Billy Hufsey.

Debbie Allen's showbusiness career began in ballet, then she worked in Broadway shows as a dancer, before adding acting and choreography to her list of achievements.

She is a tireless worker, a real pro, and though *Fame* is very hard, time-consuming work, Debbie wants to work in yet more varied fields. "This business moves so fast, you have to initiate," she says. "You have to always be looking ahead, taking advantage of your current success and planning for the future."

To this end Debbie masterminded the *Fame* stage show that toured extensively in Europe, appeared with Johnny Mathis in New York — and she's developing several scripts, one of which she wrote herself. She has also appeared in the TV movie *Women of San Quentin*, and has signed a recording contract.

Debbie thanks *Fame* for all this: "None of this would have been possible without my being on *Fame*. The series has been good to me, and I really hope that 'we're gonna live forever'. Actually, I think the series *can* go on forever. It's a good show, a realistic show, with good production values. I think it's been such an international success because it deals with young people growing up. And that's universal, whatever language is spoken."

DOWN AT THE FUNHOUSE

Holly Laird found one of the few remaining seats in the canteen and unpacked her lunch of one tuna fish salad sandwich, one boiled egg and an orange. She took a bite of her sandwich and settled back to read once again the first letter she'd had in weeks from her old school-friend, Lesley Barnes. She unfolded the white sheet of paper, and as she read an awful feeling of impending gloom and embarrassment swept through her entire body. ANYONE INTERESTED IN SEEING THE PEPSI BETHEL AUTHENTIC JAZZ THEATRE SHOULD CONTACT MISS GRANT BEFORE TUESDAY AT THE LATEST. The note was signed by Lydia Grant.

Holly swallowed hard. It was the note that Miss Grant had given her to pin up on the notice board. If the note was where the letter should have been – where was the letter? She scrambled through the contents of her bag, spilling two combs, a purse and some Kleenex onto the table. There was no sign of the letter.

Leaving her lunch on the table, Holly raced out of the room, her heart pounding. Surely she couldn't have been that absentminded, that stupid? When she saw the crowd of students laughing round the notice board she knew she could. In her haste to get a seat in the lunch room she had pinned up Lesley's letter instead of Miss Grant's note.

Holly pushed her way through the crowd.

At the board, Coco was reading out loud. "Dear Holly, what a time we had! Pity your parents had to catch us out. I don't think they really approve of me. Anyway, I'll try to get to see you when I'm in town. All my love, Les."

Holly reached up for the letter, but Coco beat her to it.

"All my love, huh?" said Coco with a mischievous smile. "I guess Les must be one cool cat. What did he do that was so bad it made your folks mad?"

"But – but –" stammered Holly.

"Still, he must be something special for you to broadcast your love over all the school," said Coco, finally handing the letter back to Holly as the rest of the crowd whooped and yelled. Holly's face grew redder and redder.

"It's not what you think –" she began lamely.

56

Danny interrupted her with some good-natured teasing. "So now you're a mind-reader as well as a fox? How do you know what we think? Or are you even more of a black sheep than we thought you were?"

Holly's embarrassment was turning to anger. They thought they were all so clever. Fox? Black sheep? If they'd all grow up a bit they might get close to the truth.

"As a matter of fact, Les is quite different to what you think," she said, pinning Miss Grant's notice up on the board.

"Has he got two heads?" asked Danny. "Four legs? Eight arms?"

"No. Les is just different."

"Well, we'll find out when he comes to visit you, won't we?" said Coco. "You will be showing him off to us, won't you? After all, if he's good enough to put up on

the notice board, he's good enough for us to meet, right? Unless you're scared that one of us beautiful girls is going to steal him from you?"

Coco danced away down the corridor, laughing. Danny led the others in the barrage of questions about her new boyfriend. By the time the music lesson started, Holly had had enough.

As Professor Shorofsky explained how the envelope of human hearing ranged from the barely audible rustling of leaves at 3 dB to the physically painful 140 dBs of a jet engine at fifteen feet, Holly cursed herself for not explaining properly. How were the others to know that Les was a girl? That in the holidays she and Holly had gone to a rock concert that finished two hours later than scheduled? That when they finally got

back, Holly's parents had been chewing the carpet with worry and were on the verge of calling the police? It had all blown over, of course, but Holly's parents, as parents often do, had put most of the blame on Les.

And now Holly had either to produce a boyfriend or admit that she'd let the others think the wrong thing. When she saw Danny grinning at her across the class her toes curled inside her sneakers and she groaned inwardly.

"I beg your pardon, Miss Laird?" asked Shorofsky.

"Nothing, professor."

"Although the acuity of the human being's ability to decipher sounds lessens with age, even someone of my advancing years is unlikely to –"

"I'm sorry, Professor Shorofsky, I was just thinking out loud."

"Please don't," said Shorofsky, wiping his glasses and holding them up to the light. "Just try and utilise that part of the body we are discussing."

"Yes, Professor."

That evening after school, Holly went to the café where Bruno worked to catch up on the lunch she had missed.

Chris was there, with Coco, and they were both looking worried. When Holly sat down with them she found out why.

"I got this friend from England," explained Chris. "He's over here on holiday for a while." Chris flipped a photograph of a handsome young man leaning on a motorbike onto the table. He was lean and muscular and his dark hair fell across his left eye.

"He wanted to look round, so I left him with some other friends of mine," Chris continued. "At least, I *thought* they were my friends. They were driving across town when a cop stopped them and a fight started. The cop got knocked out and now there's an APB on them."

"What's your friend's name?" asked Holly, studying the photograph.

"Mickey."

"Surely the cops won't know that?"

"They've got his description. I know Mickey well and I know he wouldn't harm a fly. The guys I left him with must have blown their hatches. Now all of them are on the run."

"Do you know where they're hiding out?" asked Coco.

"Nope. I said I'd meet Mickey here after school. I've just got to hope he makes it. If I can get Mickey to the cops before the cops get to Mickey, this whole thing could be straightened out."

"But we don't know where he is."

"No."

Holly ate a pizza in silence as Chris bemoaned the fact that Mickey was a stranger in town. They were all aware of how dangerous this could be, especially with the cops on his tail.

Eventually Chris stood up. "I can't wait any longer," he said. "I'm going to look for him."

"Don't be stupid, this is a big town," warned Coco.

"I know it. But I also know that Mickey is crazy about discos. He kept trying to get me to promise to take him to some of the good ones. Maybe he's hiding out in the disco crowds."

"You want me to come too?" asked Coco.

Chris looked at Holly. "We need somebody here in case Mickey rings. How about it, Holly?"

Holly tried to hide her emotions behind a sip of coffee. She didn't need this kind of interference. She didn't want to seem uncaring, but after all – Coco had made her the butt of the joke about Lesley.

"I'm sorry," she said. "I promised I'd be in early."

"That's OK," said Chris, turning back to Coco. "Now if anybody rings, you come and find me, right?"

"Right."

Chris left the café and Bruno brought two more coffees over. As Holly sipped hers she could feel Coco's eyes staring accusingly over the table at her. She was about to try and explain when Bruno returned with an excited look on his face.

"Where's Chris gone?" he asked. "I've just had Mickey on the phone."

"Chris is looking for him in the discos," said Coco.

"Which ones?"

"I don't know. He's working his way west."

"Well, Mickey's at The Funhouse on West 26th Street. He didn't sound too happy. He's

given the other guys the slip, but when I told him to turn himself in he wasn't having any."

"Thanks, Bruno," said Coco, standing up ready to leave. "I'm going straight to The Funhouse to talk to him. By the time I find Chris, Mickey might have gone."

"You're right, Coco," said Bruno, picking up Coco's half empty cup. "I'll stay here in case Chris rings."

Coco thanked Bruno again, cast a haughty glance at Holly, then walked out onto the street. As she was hurrying towards West 26th Street, she was so wrapped up with her mission that she didn't give a second glance to the tall man in the long grey overcoat, reading the paper in a doorway across the road.

But Holly, watching Coco leave with a mixture of conflicting emotions, spotted him straightaway. And when he folded up his newspaper and set out after Coco, she knew. He was a cop, and Coco was leading him straight to Mickey.

Holly took a piece of paper out of her bag and quickly wrote a note. It said, COCO – THEY'RE ON TO YOU – I'LL TAKE OVER. She ran out of the café and sprinted the opposite way round the block, hoping to catch Coco before she reached the next intersection.

Holly only just made it. Coco was waiting for the lights to change when Holly, for the first time in her life using the comedian's prat-fall she thought she was wasting her time studying, stumbled into Coco and thrust the crumpled note into her hand.

"What the –?" said Coco.

"Sshhh! Keep going!" hissed Holly, steadying herself and hurrying on.

Coco looked around her and for the first time she noticed the man in the overcoat who was tailing her. She crossed the street and then took a sharp right, away from West 26th Street.

Holly checked her purse. Thirty-six dollars twenty-two cents. Most of it was towards her rent, but this was an emergency. She hailed the first cab passing and, amazingly, it stopped.

"The Funhouse," she said, getting in.

"You got it," said the driver, a middle-aged man with a red baseball hat. "Are you a professional dancer?"

Holly laughed. As the taxi sped towards the disco she got an inkling of how it must feel to be one of the vast legion of New York's fun-loving party goers, out dancing and laughing night after night. At first the idea excited her, but she knew, deep down, that the whole scene was an illusion, that underneath the glitter and the easy friendships there was a desperate kind of loneliness that had no part in her future as a serious actress.

The taxi pulled up and Holly got out and paid the driver. She hurried, head down, past three men in white bomber jackets, then went through the mirror maze that served as an entrance to The Funhouse.

Inside, it took Holly some time to get her bearings. Ear-splitting music boomed out of the speakers and flashing lights shone intermittently on the paintings of the clowns and acrobats on the walls.

It was less crowded up there, and within minutes she saw, sitting in one of the plush chairs with his back to the wall, a young man she recognised immediately as Mickey.

"Listen, you don't know me, but I know you," she said, taking a seat next to him.

His worried frown broke into an amused smile. "That's a new line to me," he said, his bright blue eyes twinkling in the light.

"It's true," said Holly, finding it difficult not to smile herself. "I go to school with Chris – he's out looking for you right now."

"That guy has some weird friends. We got stopped for speeding and one of them, a skinny little fellow who would have to run round in a shower to get wet, started shouting police harrassment. The cop didn't like it but the kid kept on. The cop cuffed him and then the balloon went up. I was glad to get away from them."

"You're safe for now," said Holly, "but the police have got your description. Chris says if you turn yourselves in he'll be able to clear everything up."

"Well . . ." said Mickey, mulling the problem over. "I suppose that's best –"

Mickey didn't finish his sentence. Holly, having seen two policemen on the edge of the dance floor, looking over the crowds of revellers, suddenly embraced him, hiding his face from their gaze.

"Cops," she whispered. "Kiss me."

Mickey didn't need telling twice. He took Holly in his arms and kissed her gently, tenderly, watching over her shoulder as the cops continued their search. And when they gave up and left, he kept right on kissing.

"If beauty were a minute – you'd be an hour," he sighed, finally releasing her.

"You're pretty cute yourself, boy," replied Holly, slowly breaking away. "But now you've got to go to the police station."

"Can't we have just one dance?"

Holly looked down at the dance

In the middle of the floor, young men and women were slamming and breaking to the sounds of Madonna. One entire wall was covered by a huge three-dimensional clown's head which housed the DJ at the centre of its manic smile. There was no sign of Mickey.

"Hey – you wanna dance?"

Holly turned and saw one of the white jacketed men she had seen outside. She quelled the sudden fear she felt in her stomach and ran through her repertoire of roles for a suitable one to play. She finally settled on an English duch-ess that owed a lot to Barbara Stanwyck's playing in *The Lady Eve*. "I'm so frightfully, frightfully sorry, but I'm somewhat enner-vated from riding to hounds this morning. And then I got stuck on the wretched tube. I was trying to get to the Embassy to see Uncle Buffy, don't you know."

"Unh?"

"Be a dear and close your mouth," said Holly in her clipped English voice, pushing past the man and making her way through the mass of dancing couples, across the floor and up onto the balcony.

floor. The frantic dancing had stopped and Smokey Robinson's milk chocolate vocals were flying on a cloud of violins as couples moved slowly together.

"No time," she said, snapping her act together. "Let's go."

When they reached the police station they were surprised to see Chris there, talking to Coco and the man in the long grey coat. Mickey was taken to an upstairs room to explain things, and before he went he took time out to thank Holly once again. With a long, lingering kiss in the middle of the police station. . . .

"Okay, you guys," said the policeman eventually. "Break it up."

As he led Mickey up the stairs Coco linked her arm with Holly's. "That's enough excitement for one night, girl," she said, smiling. "Now I'm taking you home."

"Coco," said Holly as they walked down the police station steps, "there's something I want to tell you . . . about that letter from Les . . ."

"I'm sorry I made fun of you."

"It's just that –"

"Forget it, girl – you're going home."

The following day, as Chris stood on the street outside the school, rapping like a Texas cattle auctioneer, and Danny, Doris and Coco danced in a tight circle, Holly turned the corner into the street more convinced than ever that, with a lot of hard work and a little bit of luck, she was going to make it. She was smiling to herself when she climbed the stairs.

"You look like you had a good night," called Danny. Holly ignored him. "Another date with the four-armed, two-headed Les? Or was it the creature from the Black Lagoon?"

"Neither," said Holly calmly. Why should she worry? She was young, free, and on her way. And she'd already had a phone call from Mickey. Two seats at the Ziegfeld for the new Richard Gere movie sounded like a pretty good way to spend the evening.

"Let me see . . ." Danny went on, imitating an absent-minded professor. "It wasn't the creature . . . it wasn't the Beast from Fifty Fathoms . . . I know for a fact he's hot for the Werewolf Woman . . . so . . . don't tell me, Holly . . . not Gorgozilla the vampire cheese? He's too old for you and he can't –"

"Danny," said Coco, quietly but firmly interrupting.

"Yes?"

"Shut up."

And while Danny clutched his heart like a mortally-wounded soldier, they all filed into the building to start another day.

The Stars of Fame:
GENE ANTHONY RAY

Gene Anthony Ray was born and brought up in New York, and dancing has been an important part of his life ever since he can remember. "While I was growing up I was dancing all the time," he says. "I didn't take any classes; I learned by watching my friends and by watching TV — I just learned to do it. I performed all the time."

Gene did attend the School of Performing Arts (the school *Fame* is based on), but he was kicked out in his first year. That didn't stop him auditioning for a part in the *Fame* movie, though, and despite his lack of formal dance training he won out over the 3,000 others who were also trying out.

There's a lot of Gene in the part he was chosen for, Leroy Johnson. "The role in Fame was almost written for me before they even knew that I was around. Even though I didn't have any acting experience in the film it wasn't hard to play the part because most of it was me. I can really relate to the part because I have been a Leroy Johnson in my younger days — though I'm not like that now!"

Gene got rave reviews for his part in the film, so he was the obvious choice to continue the role on television. "One thing I learned in dancing is that an encore is as important as the original performance," he says. "That's why I liked the idea of reprising the Leroy role for tv. It's like putting on blue jeans and a comfortable pair of shoes . . . you *know* it fits."